THE H

Eamon Kelly

MERCIER PRESS

MERCIER PRESS
PO Box 5, 5 French Church Street, Cork
24 Lower Abbey Street, Dublin 1

© Eamon Kelly, 1978
ISBN 0 85342 929 4
First Published in 1978
Reprinted 1984
Reprinted 1992

The Holy Well was originally published under the title *The Rub of a Relic*. *The Rub of a Relic*, Eamon Kelly's third storytelling evening, was first presented by The Abbey Theatre at The Everyman Theatre, Cork, on 9 January 1978. It was directed by Michael Colgan.

Illustrations by Kevin Scally

Printed in Ireland by Colour Books Ltd.

CONTENTS

THE HOLY WELL

I remember one time lining up for a drink at the holy well. The lame and the blind and the halt were there. I noticed that the man out before me had a sore face, his lips broken out and his mouth all to one side. I didn't know how I was going to drink out of the ponny after him. But faith, small and all as I was, when it came to my turn, taking the tin mug in my left hand, and dipping it down, I took a swig out of it. I looked up and there was the man with the sore face watching me, and he said:

'Ah ha, I see you are a *ciotóg* like myself'!

You could be cured of anything that time at the holy well. Different wells for different cures. Wether's Well for warts, Batt's Well for sore eyes, Brideswell for the colic and Ben's Well for the back. The old people swore by Ben's Well, anything to do with the bladder or the kidneys. They claimed if you drank a couple of saucepans of that for nine mornings running without a bite going inside your lips, it would dry you up no matter how quick your frequency!

But the holy well never dries up. The hottest day in the summer time, that's the day the holy well is bubbling over. A landlord one time objected to the people going through his fields the day of the pattern — look at that for venom! He filled in the holy well. But he was the sorry man. The spring cannot be repressed! That night the well came up through the hearth inside in his own house and put out the fire on him! The Saints had power that time. There was Saint Laitíoran and she had two sisters, Saints Lasaire and Iníon Bhuí. You'd hardly ever hear of three saints in the one family now! Saint Lasaire was connected with the holy well in Cullen and her day is in July. It was said of Laitíoran that when the fire'd go out in the convent she'd cross the road to the forge and bring back the live coals in her apron, and such was her sanctity the coals wouldn't burn it.

One morning on lifting her apron a bit of her skirt came up with it, and the smith, so much wouldn't pass him, remarked on her dainty ankles, and for a split second she took pleasure in the remark. This was noticed above and the coals burned a hole down through her apron! She was so incensed at having incurred the wrath of heaven that she told the smith: 'A time will come when the sound of the anvil will not be heard in the village of Cullen!' And they tell me there's no forge there down to this day.

There's always a trout in the holy well. And a very mysterious fish. In penal times the people used get married in the houses and at night too, and the priest would remain on until after the supper. Now in one place the woman in charge of the cooking came and said that the pot she had hanging over the fire, and that should have come to the boil long ago, was as cold as when she put it down. The priest wanted to know where she got the water and she said: 'Mickeen brought it from the holy well.' And of course, that was a very wrong thing to do. To go to the holy well, to go to any well after dark, the old people held it wasn't right! The priest came up and lifted the lid of the pot and there was the trout swimming around inside. He told 'em to spill him out into a vessel and bring him back to the holy well. This they did and they had no trouble with their water after.

And before it goes out of my head I want to tell about this blackguard that took the trout out of the holy well and put him down on the griddle. Like Fionn Mac Cumhaill tasting the salmon of knowledge, he thought that sampling the little trout would improve all his faculties of body and mind. But there was a hop knocked out of him, before he had time to turn the trout it hopped off the griddle and went plop-ity, plop, plop, plop, plop-ity down the floor out the back door and into the well. And that trout bears the burnt marks of the griddle on one side down to this day, and when you are doing the rounds at that penitential place, and when you come to drink at the holy well, if it is your good fortune to see the burnt side of the trout you could be cured of anything from wind-gall to carbuncles!

The holy well is nearly always in a lonesome place. There is a ruin there, or a graveyard and in places it was part of the penitential round to say a prayer at the family grave. At the nearside of Carraig an Adhmaid, where some of my neighbours are buried, the rock is very near the skin of the ground, and if you are burying a man there it would tighten you to put him down four feet and indeed some of 'em are only gone down three. And we'll say now, if there was a lot of traffic to one grave in a short space of time, the people'd find it hard to put back the boards of the old coffins and the bones, for they wouldn't all fit. Over in Carraig an Adhmaid I remember there used to be a heap of skulls in the corner. And bloody frightening they were too for a small child to be looking at 'em, and they thrown this way and that and they grinning

7

up at you!

At that time there was a tailor in the village and he had an apprentice, the devils own airy card, and the two of 'em'd be sitting back to back up on the table every night sewing away, and the kitchen full of neighbours, for tailors have the name of being jolly. One night the conversation turned to things of the spirit and they were talking about the *bean sí* and the *bád sí* and the *ceol sí* and the *púcaí*. There was a great dread of the supernatural at the time but the tailor's apprentice was afraid of nothing. He said he was out all hours and never saw anything uglier than himself — and you'd think it'd be hard for him.

'All right, so,' says the tailor, 'would you go up to the graveyard this hour of the night?'

'I would,' says the apprentice.

'But,' says the tailor, 'would you bring me down a skull out of it?'

'I would,' says the apprentice, 'but I won't do it for nothing. I'll have to be paid for it. What will you give me?'

The tailor wanted to appear spunky in front of his neighbours so he said:

'All right. You have three of your five years apprenticeship done. I'll give the two years off. If you do what you say I'll give you your indentures in the morning and you can go away a journeyman!'

'A bargain,' says the apprentice, and he hopped off the table, stuck the two legs into the shoes and off out the door with him.

When he was gone the tailor got sorry. He said to himself that the apprentice was blackguard enough to do it. And if that same apprentice left him he'd be very short-handed. So he hopped off the table, stuck his legs into his shoes and made out the door after him.

8

"Leave down my head!"

The tailor being a local man knew all the near ways to the graveyard and he was there before the apprentice and ducked down behind a tombstone. And the sort of a night it was, you had clouds racing across the face of the moon, so that you had light moving across the graveyard, then darkness, and then light again showing the faces of the statues and the drunken crosses. The tailor thought they were moving and you wouldn't blame him for going bocketty at the knees, so that it was a great relief to him when the apprentice hopped in over the wall.

The clouds cleared from the face of the moon as the apprentice walked over to where the heap of skulls was. He picked up a skull, and if he did, the tailor, altering his voice, and he could do it, he'd get a medal for it, said:

'Leave down my head!'

The apprentice dropped the skull the same as if it was a hot coal. He looked around but when he couldn't see the owner of the voice he bent down and picked up another one.

And the tailor altering his voice again, said:

'Leave down my head!'

The apprentice was just about to drop the skull when he changed his mind, and looking in the direction of the voice, he said:

'Ah, bad luck to it, you couldn't have two heads.'

Off with him out and over the wall and as he walked along between the trees he heard the twigs breaking on the ground behind him. Of course he didn't know it was the tailor was after him. He ran like hell back to the house and throwing the skull up on the table he went in hide behind the press shouting:

'Bolt the door quick, the fellow that owns the head is after me.'

THE CITY

Ar maidin inné sea do dhearcas an stuaire cailín,
Her limbs were complete and she neatly clothed in
   green,
A mala ba chaol is a béilín ba ró-mhilis bhí,
And I knew by her gazing she'd play the game called
   'Hide and go Seek'.

Do dhruideas fé'n mbé agus d'iarras di póigín nú trí,
She answered and said: 'Young man you are making
   too free.'
Sé dúras fé'n mbé: 'Ná tiocfása liomsa mar mhnaoi,
And I'll teach you to play the game called 'Hide and
   go Seek'.

Do fhreagair an bhé go béasach, banúil, binn;
'I'm anxious to play that game of which you do speak'.
*Ar an sagart do ghlaomar is d'fháisc sé go daingean
   an chuing,*
And I taught her to play the game called 'Hide and go
   Seek'.[1]

That song was made up over a hundred years ago
when the people spoke two languages and the women
had to take lessons! You'd hear it at Gougane the day
of the pattern, or at Carraig an Adhmaid where there's
another holy well, but the well I had most recourse to

11

when I was small was Cathair Chrobh Dhearg — The City.

The City was ever famous and so old as a penitential place that people were going there on pilgrimage long before Moses brought the Israelites out of Egypt. The City is about forty-five spades across, I measured it, and built in circular form surrounded by a stone embankment now falling, but in its hey-day the wailing wall of Jerusalem was nothing to it!

The first day of May was the pattern day at the City. The water of the holy well had very special properties and was in great demand for curing cattle and blessing crops and many favours were granted in that line. There was a belief then that the hare milked the cow on May morning, and that before sunrise evil people pulled a rope over the grass to gather to their own dairies the good of another man's land. And to guard against these *piseoga* cattle from far and near were driven inside the wall of the City on May Eve and there they'd spend the night, so that the bulls would get the benefit and the cows retain the profit for the coming year!

Away back in Crobh Dhearg's time, he was the pagan with the red hand, a valuable bull was stolen out of the City in the middle of the night and driven over the hill. The thief left his tracks and he was caught, and the print of his foot and the print of the bull's foot and the mark of the cudgel can be seen on the face of the rock down to this day.

The City is situated at the butt of the Paps, the famous twin mountains. In Irish they are called An Dá Chích Danann, the breasts of the goddess Dana, and they'd remind you of only the one thing . . . well the two things. And from above Gneeveguilla if the day is clear, looking south, you can see the goddess lying

12

back taking a little snooze for herself. Well these two, they are about a mile apart and the Slugadal flows down between 'em. There is a corkscrew road made up there now and the tourists don't have to turn their heads to look at the scenery. The Paps are nearly three thousand feet above sea-level, and so well made, Glory be to the maker, that there's only ten feet in the difference in their height — as one man said to me:

'The Goddess is lying a little to one side!'

At the top of the Paps there are two man-made mounds. Some say they were put there by the engineers of the Down Survey, and some say they were put there in olden times to mark the place where Fionn Mac Cumhaill put his feet, when he bent down over the Slugadal to wash his face in Loch na Gaoithe! It was at the top of the Paps Fionn's warriors had their look-out, and their vision was so keen they could see the stranger coming up the Shannon or into Bantry Bay. It was from up there the Greek ship bringing Caol an Iarrainn to Ireland was first spotted and a signal, warning of its approach, was sent to the Fianna camped down on the Hill of Howth.

As the ship landed in Howth a door at the side opened, and the Fianna expected to see an army come marching out, and great indeed was their surprise when only one man appeared. And there is no man in the world today as well-built as he was, or as tall as he was, for his head would touch the rafter. He came up and challenged the Fianna to fight man to man in single combat. Fionn, sparring for wind, when he saw the size of the man and the fierce sword he had, said:

'Before we turn our hand to fighting in this country, we have seven days of racing, jumping and putting the shot. In which of these activities would you like to engage?'

'Racing,' says the Hero from Greece, 'and if I am out-done on the track I'll go home and do no damage here.'

Fionn, greatly relieved, set out to find Caoilte Mac Rónáin, the champion runner of the Fianna. He hadn't gone far when he saw approaching him a man of outlandish appearance. This man told Fionn his name was Bodach an Chóta Lachtna, or the Clown in the Grey Top Coat, and that he had come to race the Hero from Greece. When the Fianna saw Fionn coming with this man it gave them as much as they could do to keep a straight face, for Bodach an Chóta Lachtna was a big ugly laughing clown with two legs under him like the two masts of a ship, and two shoes like two rowing boats spattering barrelfuls of mud all round him. And the hem of his long, grey, top coat was so caked with mud that, as he ran, it hit against the backs of his collops making a loud report that could be heard a mile away!

The race was from Sliabh Luachra at the butt of the Paps to the hill of Howth, and the two warriors walked the track down the night before, so that they'd know the way back tomorrow. When they landed below Bodach an Chóta Lachtna went to the wood, cut down a tree and made a house, even though he was only going to be there for one night, and he went to the wood, cut down a tree and made a spit, and he went to the wood, killed a boar, and with one clout of his sword he split the wild boar from the top of his nose to the tip of his tail and put half of him turning on the spit over the fire.

He ran north then, jumped across the Shannon to Lord Glen Inchiquin's place in the county Clare and brought back a table and two chairs, two bags of white bread and two barrels of wine. When he arrived back the half of the wild boar was cooked so he set the table and called in the Hero from Greece, but he said he wouldn't be seen dead in the same house as a big ugly laughing clown.

'In that case,' says the Bodach, 'it was idle for me to bring a second chair all the ways from the County Clare!'

So he fell in, finished the half of the wild boar, one bag of white bread and washed the whole lot down with a barrel of wine. He went out then cut a *beart* of rushes and spreading the rushes on the flag of the fire he bunked down for the night. In the morning the sun rising lit up the two Paps, and the birds singing woke the Hero from Greece. He rose and called Bodach an Chóta Lachtna to say it was time to set out in the race.

'Go away,' the Bodach told him, 'I'll get up to you!'

The Hero from Greece, glad of the handicap, set out and Bodach an Chóta Lachtna went back to bed for another hour. He got up then and put the other half of the wild boar turning on the spit over the fire and when that was done he fell in and finished it, and the second bag of white bread and washed it all down with the second barrel of wine. Then he collected up the bones and put 'em inside the lining of his long, grey coat and set out in the race, picking a bone as he went and, when it was clean, throwing it back over his shoulder.

Going up by Buttevant he passed out the Hero from Greece. When he came to Cashel he saw apple trees growing at the side of the road, and as he was hungry again he sat down to have a feed. Up came the Hero from Greece and he said to Bodach an Chóta Lachtna:

'There are bits and pieces and tatters of your old coat hanging out of every bush from here down to Killmallock!'

Bodach an Chóta Lachtna got up and walked the

...he went flying past the Hero from Greece.

road back, picking the bits and pieces off the bushes, and when he had them all, he took out a needle and thread and sewed them back into the coat until it was as good as it was before, and that wouldn't be saying much for it. Then he set out in the race in earnest, and half way up through Kildare he went flying past the Hero from Greece. He was going so fast now that he passed out the wind in front of him and the wind behind him couldn't get up to him.

At Celbridge he saw a brake of briars. The blackberries were out so he sat down to have another feed. The blackberries tasted so sweet he said he'd bring some home, but as he had no container he took off his long grey top coat, sewed it down the middle and across the bottom and made a sack of it. He filled the blackberries in at the neck, and he was just about to catch the two sleeves and swing it on his back, when he noticed that he had not a scrat of clothes on under the coat. He gathered more blackberries and bruising 'em between his hands he rubbed the juice into himself all over so that he wouldn't appear too naked going through Dublin.

He set out and when the Fianna warriors on the Hill of Howth saw him afar off they said:

'As sure as anything this is the Hero from Greece having killed Bodach an Chóta Lachtna on the way and he is bringing him on his back!'

But as he came nearer they saw who they had. Bodach an Chóta Lachtna came up and ordered five sacks of flour and three churns of buttermilk. He made a huge cake and cutting it in two he spilled the coatful of blackberries into the middle. He put the cake on an iron platform over a huge fire and when it was baked he saw the Hero from Greece running up. He was so vexed at being outdone by a big ugly laughing clown, that he made for his sword, but before he had time to draw it, Bodach an Chóta Lachtna threw the cake at him, and it met the Hero from Greece in the side of the face with such force that it spun his head right round — he was the first man in the world able to look down his own back!

Then taking him by the shoulder he ran him down the side of the Hill of Howth into the ship, and giving the ship one kick he put it five leagues out in the channel. Bodach an Chóta Lachtna turned and walked up the hill, and the Fianna watching saw him change into the fine figure of a respectable man. They wined him and dined him for seven days and seven nights. When he left there were some warriors who would go so far as to say that the stranger was none other than Mananán Mac Lir, who came in the disguise of an ugly, laughing clown to relieve 'em in their hardest hour!

1. It was yesterday morning I spied the tall beautiful maid, her limbs were complete and she neatly clothed in green, her brow it was fine, her lips too sweet, and I knew by her gazing she'd play the game called 'Hide and go Seek'. I approached the maid and I asked her for a kiss or three, she answered and said: 'Young man you are making too free'. I said to the maid: 'Wouldn't you be my wife', and I'll teach you to play the game called 'Hide and go Seek'. The maid answered politely, modestly, sweetly: 'I'm anxious to play that game of which you do speak'. The priest we called and he tightly tied the knot, and I taught her to play the game called 'Hide and go Seek'.

THE GOLDEN STEED

There was a King in Ireland one time and another King in Greece and when they were young they were in the same school together in France. You had a very up-to-date academy there at the time for training young kings. It is not fighting they were like the other two but the very best of friends, so much so that the two young men would come to Ireland for their summer holidays, and at Christmas time they'd go to Greece.

When they were getting their indentures in that school they made a solemn promise that they would not let any grass grow under their feet until they would meet again. They went back to their own homes and after a time the old Kings died. Then they had to take over the thrones. In a year or so women were got for 'em and they married, and between that and running the country, they had no time to meet. An only son is all the King of Greece had, and an only daughter was all that was born to the King of Ireland. When the son of the King of Greece was filling out into a young man his father called him and his mother down in the room one day and said:

'It is a long time now since I saw my old friend over in Ireland. I wonder how he is getting on! Now that the war is over and the blackguards put down we have some time on our hands and why don't we go over and

19

see him!!'

The son and the mother agreed with him, and they called the sailors, sat into the boat and set out.

About the same time here in Ireland the King called his wife and daughter down in the room and said:

'It is a long time now since I saw my old friend over in Greece, I d' know in the world how he is getting on! Now that we have the hay in the haggard, the turf in the rick and the pig in the tub, we have some time on our hands, so why don't we go over and see him!'

Well, the two women were all out for this big excursion, so they called the sailors, sat into the boat and set out. Now, when the King of Greece landed in Ireland he was told that the King of Ireland was gone to Greece, and when the King of Ireland landed in Greece he heard that the King of Greece was gone to Ireland. It was an awful mix-up and was in all the papers at the time. They turned around for home and the ships met in the middle of the ocean. They all went on board the Irish ship. The King of Greece said to his own sailors:

'Be fishing around there for the space of a week so that we will have something to show by our time.'

Well the two Kings had so much to talk about when they met, and so had the women when they got to know one another. And the young people . . . the ships at that time, you couldn't swing a cat in 'em, long and narrow, so that they were thrown very much into their own company. The upshot of all this was that the daughter of the King of Ireland came to her mother saying:

'Faith, he's after me now to marry him!'

The mother was upset at this for the daughter was barely sixteen, so she went and spoke to the two Kings. They were divarted at the news. This was the very thing they were hoping for. A match would bring the two families closer together, so the King of Ireland took his wife one side and whispered to her:

'Will you whist! Can't they wait until she is eighteen years of age. He can marry her then and it won't spoil her growth.'

This was agreed and the two young people made it up in secret that the son of the King of Greece would come to Ireland for her the day she would be eighteen years of age. The King of Greece, his wife and son went into their own ship and the two parties set out for home.

Ah, but look at the queer turn things can take! The daughter of the King of Ireland was hardly seventeen years when her mother got sick. There was no one below in the room when the last breath was going out of her but the King. She made him promise he would look after the little girl, and she made him promise that he wouldn't marry again. But if he couldn't contain himself, to marry only the woman that the ring on her finger would fit. She gave him the ring into his palm, and then turning her face to the wall she went out like a light!

The day after the funeral the King came to his daughter and said:

'Be putting your mother's clothes together until we divide 'em up among the poor. I'm going hunting!'

And when the daughter was rummaging in the press she found her mother's ring and she put it on her finger like any young girl'd do. When the father came in to his supper that night whatever look he gave he saw the ring on her, and taking her by the hand he tried to pull the ring off her finger.

'What have you done!' he said, telling her all about the pledge he had made to her mother. 'You'll have to

21

marry me now!'

'I won't marry you.' And then she thought for a little bit. 'I won't marry you until you bring me a dress of shining shillings!'

That took him a long time to get, but in the end he brought it to her and she said:

'I won't marry you now either until you bring me a dress of feathers and no two feathers from the same bird in the air!'

That took an even longer time to get, but in the end he brought it to her and she said:

'I'll marry you when you bring me a horse made of gold.'

He went away and he put the horse making and when she found out who the smith was, she went to him in secret and she said:

'Whatever money my father is giving you, I'll give you as much more if you can put a door in the side of the horse in a form that a person can go in or out and with a lock on the inside.'

The smith claimed that would be knacky, but that he'd try it, and when she went back to him in a month's time, there was the door on the side of the horse as handy as a pocket in a shirt only not half as noticeable. She told the smith then the day on which he should have the horse finished. When the horse was made the King had him brought to the palace and himself and his daughter were to be married the following morning.

That night the daughter of the King of Ireland went to no bed. She remained up baking and when she had enough food, she gathered up her few belongings and in the dark stole out and went into the horse and put on the bolt from the inside, and only that the smith had the good fortune to make the horse with his mouth opened, and another vent elsewhere, she'd have smothered inside in him.

When the King came down in the morning the daughter was nowhere to be found. He called the soldiers and the servants and after looking in the palace they went out around the countryside searching for her. When they were all gone a ship came into the harbour, and who was it but the son of the King of Greece coming for her, for this was the very day on which she was eighteen years of age.

The young man and his sailors came up and finding the door of the Palace open they went in and looked through all the rooms; when there was no one in the house they went out in the back yard. There was no one there but the hen woman. She was full of talk for the strangers. She told 'em all about the promise, the dress of shining shillings and the dress of feathers.

'And the last thing the daughter asked her father for,' she said, 'was a horse made of gold and that's him standing there.'

The son of the King of Greece walked around the golden steed saying: 'And a damn nice purty too!' Then turning to his sailors he said:

'Seeing as she isn't here herself we'll bring the horse home so as to have something to show by our time!'

The sailors lifted up the golden steed and brought him to the ship and when they landed over in Greece they put the horse standing on a platform near the gable of the house. It looked well there and people were coming from far and near to see it. In a couple of days' time when the hunger picked the daughter of the King of Ireland, she came out of the horse and went to whoever was in charge looking for a job, and the job she got was minding the fowl in the yard — they used to have peacocks there and everything. There was a small house going with the job. Very well why, the son of the King of Greece was drilling his soldiers around the yard the following day, when he heard a music box playing inside the small house. He ran over to the window and looked in and when he saw who was inside, he was trying to break down the door to get into her. But there is no accounting for women. She wouldn't open the door for him!

'Who are you?' she said.

'I'm the son of the King of Greece,' says he.

'You're not,' says she, 'because if you were you'd have more manners!'

He took a turn then, got a fit and had to take to the bed. He was bad and the doctors came and they couldn't do anything for him. One day he said to his mother:

'There's only one thing that will bring me any relief now, and that is, if the girl in the small house in the yard would bring me up a drink of water.'

The mother said in her own mind that that would be a cheap enough cure, so she gave a half cup of new milk with a hot drop spilled into it out of the kettle to one of the servants saying:

'Bring that to the one outside and tell her to take it up to him!'

When the daughter of the King of Ireland went into the room above he told her to bolt the door, and she seeing the woebegone look of him knew that he was really in love with her and the two of 'em nearly went out of their skins with delight. He kept her inside and the following morning the marriage was arranged. Everyone that was anyone was at the wedding and I'd be there myself, but of course if I was there that time I wouldn't be here now, and if I was same I'd be the crabbed little old lad with a beard away down to my toes!

DOING THE ROUNDS

From eight o'clock in the morning on the 'first of May at the City, the roads 'd be black with people going to the holy well. They'd be coming down the Slugadal and down the side of the mountain like a human waterfall, some men on horseback, their women up behind 'em riding *cúlóg*. At that hour the beggars would have already taken up their positions. You'd see them sitting along the brow of the road, the blind with placards around their necks, the deformed displaying a withered hand, an undeveloped leg, an old shin wound or a running sore. They'd frighten the wits out of you as they shouted out to draw attention to their affliction, and God would have to be very deaf if he didn't hear 'em calling a blessing from Heaven on those who put a penny in the hat.

Tents 'd be set up around the City where women 'd be selling cakes and candy, liquorice and lemonade, and there would be another tent in a secret place where you could get some of the home brew laced with goats' milk — that's the lad that'd put a gimp on you!

But no one 'd touch the drink until the body was mortified, and it was mortification in those days. Use 'nt they do the rounds barefoot, and in some penitential places they'd walk on their knees and the men would have to fold up their trousers . . . like the man that was late for his wedding, the alarmer didn't go off, and when he woke and saw the cut of the clock, he got into the new suit, and ran across the nearway to the Chapel. Crossing a ploughed field the bottom of his trousers was getting all dirty so he folded the legs up above his knees. When he came out in front of the chapel they were all gone in and he got so excited he forgot to readjust the trousers, he ran up the chapel to the altar where herself was waiting, and the priest said:

'Leave down your trousers!'

He looked at his bride to be, and he looked at the people. He got as red as a turkey cock. The blackguards were ribbing him all the week, saying that there was a new rite now in matrimony and God only knows what they'd be asking him to do. The people were beginning to smile in the house of God, and the priest getting very impatient said to him again:

'Leave down your trousers!'

'If it is all the same to you father,' says he, 'I'd rather do it the old way!'

To walk on their knees the men had to fold up their trousers and the women had to take off their good skirts and put them on the wall of the City. Clever women would put their shoes down on the skirt, so that it wouldn't be blown away, for it can be very windy up there. Then the women blessing themselves would flounce out their flannel petticoats, down they'd go on their knees and they were off! At that time they used to talk about this man doing the rounds. He had two fat knees on him like a bullock you'd be stall feeding, and whatever he had done out of the way he had his head down and his eyes shut praying out loud as he walked with his muddy knees on a skirt that had blown down off the wall. A man nearby whispered to him:

'Lift up that skirt!'

'I will not,' he said, 'it is for doing that I'm doing this!'

26

"Leave down your trousers!"

Three rounds you gave outside the wall at the City, moving with the sun, praying as you went and talking to no one. Then you came through a breach in the wall and you did three more rounds inside, these rounds getting more complicated as you went along, but not as complicated as the rounds are over at Carraig an Adhmaid. You'd want to be a mathematician to do the rounds in Carraig an Adhmaid!

First there was the Confiteor, then the Apostles Creed, the Prayer to the Patron Saint, seven Our Fathers and seven Hail Marys, the prayers of the round, a decade of the Glorious, Joyful or Sorrowful Mystery as you began with four rounds outside the gate. Two in the big circle and two in the small circle, where Abbey's Hive was, since stolen out of it and brought back to Dingle, until you'd stoop under the flags to Abbey's kitchen. Here with the prayer pebble you'd make the sign of the Cross seven times in the stone and from doing this down the years the cross is worn deep into the pillar stone. That done you went inside the gate and you had seventeen stations in all to do before you finished the round by drinking at the holy well.

Then if you had a mind to go and have a drink at another well down the street, or if you didn't have the inclination to do another round — and the more rounds the more grace — at that time you could buy a round. There were women there for that purpose. Use 'nt they come from Millstreet to the City and from Macroom to Carraig an Adhmaid ... Nelly Grey, Hannie Dónailín Lynch and Molly Currans. Sure Molly'd do a round for you for a shilling — three rounds for a half-a-crown. Molly claimed if you gave her enough money she'd get all belonging to you out of Purgatory, I don't know how it was that she didn't cause another Reformation!

Molly was a sort of *bean Chonnachtach,* a wise woman of the roads. She lived in a small cabin. She had nothing in the world only a goat for the colouring for the tea, and a few fowl for the fresh egg in the morning. You wouldn't give much at all for her if you saw her on the road, but the day of the pattern she was done up to the nines. She had a tartan jacket, navy skirt, button boots and a gingham apron with a big pocket for the book and the pencil to take down the rounds and another pocket for the money. Around her shoulders she had a damn fine fol-a-me-ding of a little shawl. And her hair, and she had a fine *mothal* of it, piled up on top of her head and held in position by a semi-circular comb like the arch of a bridge. And standing there on a mound over the holy well she made as big an impression on the people as if she were a bishop!

And a man told me, and a man I could believe, that the evening of the pattern she'd lump all the rounds in the book into one, and with the money she'd go down to the public house and get plastered. The following day according to him you wouldn't give tuppence for her. I saw her myself, and I a small lad, her hair flying in the wind, the brown stains of the porter on her mouth and she dancing barefoot around a bonfire that was lit below at the butt of the village the first time that De Valera went into power in 1932.

The sods of turf steeped in paraffin oil blazing on tops of three prong pikes drove Molly out of her nut with excitement. She took off her black shawl and sent it flying through the air until it landed on top of the bonfire. There was a momentary eclipse while the flames worked their way up through the shawl. A shower of sparks went up to the elements bringing with

29

it a mighty cheer. Wasn't that great *grá* for Dev! But Molly was the sorry woman the following morning and cold to boot, and no shawl came down from the Government.

One trouble never comes alone — didn't Molly's goat get killed on the railway and she cried as much after the goat as she did after the shawl, but relief wasn't far off. A farmer's wife that had been ailing for some time died in the district. The custom was at that time, that you'd give the clothes of the person who died to a poor man or woman to wear for three Sundays going to Mass and pray for the dear departed. Some widows'd find it hard enough to get even the poorest of men to wear the dead husband's clothes. Moreover, if you knew the husband! The Lord save us, maybe he died of galloping consumption. Then to get around the *piseog* some poor widows'd make a bundle of the husband's clothes and hiding the bundles under their shawls they'd bring them for three Sundays to Mass, and say a prayer for the dead man's soul. Often those bundles would be forgotten on the church seat or left up on the baptismal font, where they'd be found by Father O'. You'd have pity for the priests that time and all they had to put up with. Father O' would be so incensed at the prevalence of pagan practices in his parish that he'd throw the clothes over the cliff down into the river.

After the funeral of the farmer's wife, Molly went to the house and she got the shawl, a lovely beige, Paisley shawl with a dark brown diamondy pattern around the bottom of it and an abundance of tassels. The first Sunday she wore it to Mass, Molly went up to the front seat. For all the world it was the opening of a mission, and the holy father who was giving the sermon had a beard, a damn fine chin wag. Oh, a lovely *meigeall* that used to go up and down as he was talking. Pausing for breath in the middle of the sermon he looked down and there was Molly in floods of tears below, and I suppose he was gratified in a way that his sermon was having an effect even on one person in the congregation — it was about sudden death and sin and the hot reception that's waiting for us all. The missioner was waiting outside at the chapel gate when the people were coming out. Of course he saw Molly, you couldn't miss her, her eyes were still red. He went over to her and said:

'Well, my good woman, what was it in my sermon you found so moving?'

And she said: 'All of it, father.'

'But,' says he, 'what was it that made you cry?'

'Oh, father,' says she, 'every time I looked up at you and saw your beard wagging it reminded me of my little goat that died last week!'

Seven Our Fathers and seven Hail Marys and we are inside the wall where we come to the mound, about the ninth station. You make the sign of the Cross here too, and on either side from the circular motion of the prayer pebble there are two hollows, like the inside of a basin, worn deep into the rock. There's a perfect circle cut into a flag over at the City. Whatever that signifies? You can be sure it wasn't ratified by the Council of Trent. On that mound you'd leave a token. A safety pin, a hairpin, a button off your clothes. It would have to be from your person, a nail you'd have in your pocket, a match, a piece of a rosary beads, a holy medal or a wing-nut off your bicycle. You'd see every class of a thing there. I saw a sparking plug, a child'd nipple, a man's tie, a woman's garter, a hurley stick and a crutch, all together in the one place!

The men and the women 'd tear strips out of the

lining of their clothes, or pull a thread out of a ravelling *gansey*, and the girls 'd take ribbons out of their hair and tie 'em to the branches of the tree at the holy well. When the pattern 'd be over that tree'd be festooned with *giobals*, pennies and ha'pennies driven into the bark, and a load of crutches there — if you broke 'em up they'd keep you in firing for a week. For there were cures!

NELL CASEY

A man and a woman came by train and it was Hegarty brought them up in the jennet and car from the station to the City. And the woman was not good, the man was a pity by her, for she had no control of direction. Instead of moving with the people paying the rounds, she was more backing into 'em. Going down by Duggan's car-house coming up to the third round, she straightened a bit and went through the breach in the wall. She finished the rounds inside and drank at the holy well. Then all of a sudden like a greyhound that'd see a hare, a scatter came in her limbs, and she raced around inside the City as loose and as limber as any young girl there, throwing her hands to heaven and thanking God for being cured. She went over to the tent and bought an apron-full of cakes and candy and handed 'em around to the people, and she brought another apron-full down in the jennet and car to Hegarty's children. They were thanking God too. They thought it was another miracle. Christmas on the first of May.

But some people could be going to the holy well and rubbed with the relic every day in the week and they couldn't be cured. There was this man and his name was Casey and he had three daughters. Fine girls they were too. He needn't be one sign ashamed to be seen walking after 'em up the chapel any Sunday to Mass. And indeed he used to be a bit late so that he would be seen walking after 'em. At that time all daughters was a bit of an encumbrance to a man. Where would he get fortunes and where would he get men for 'em.

Casey's house took fire of a Christmas night. The cat to knock over the candle, they had straw inside after making the crib, and the place went up in flames. Casey and the wife and the three daughters were only barely outside the front door when the thatched roof crashed in sending a shower of sparks up to the elements. They were lucky. They came out of it without a scratch, except that the eldest daughter Nell by the dint of fright lost her power of speech. She was in a *balbhán* by him.

He brought her to this holy well and to that holy well; he brought her to the City the first of May and to Carraig an Adhmaid at Whitsun. It was no good. Then he brought her to the doctor. The doctor couldn't knock a *gíocs* out of her, so he brought her to the quack doctor near Scartaglin that had the name of licking a green lizard and was supposed to have the cure in his tongue. But the quack doctor explained to Casey that he couldn't do anything for her, for when Nell wasn't burned any place there was no place for him to lick.

In the heel of the hunt he brought her to a specialist in Cork and after paying the man a big fee, the price of a calf, do you know what the specialist told Casey — that Nell would never talk again unless she got a similar fright. Casey said he loved his daughter very much but it did not extend as far as burning another house over her!

The other two girls got married, he had no trouble getting rid of 'em, but there was no demand for Nell on

34

account of she couldn't talk. And I thought that was funny! There was a huckster's shop at the side of the road, and a very knowledgeable woman at the head of it; she had the name of bringing many a happy couple together. Casey used to get the small things there. He'd get the big groceries in town. He was in the shop one day and he said to the little woman if she could at all to be on the look out for a suitable partner for Nell. She said she would. Who should call into the shop the following day by Jeremiah O'Sullivan that lived a few miles up, and when she was papering up the few commands for him the little woman said:

'How long is your wife dead now, Jeremiah?'

'Three years, Hanna,' he said.

'And I suppose,' says she, 'you'll be taking in a young girl this spring. You have a fine farm of land and you are a young man yet, young enough anyway.'

'I woe not, Hanna,' he said.

'And why so?'

'I loved my last wife very much,' he said, 'but from the day I put the ring on her finger until the day she went out the door in the box from me, she talked twenty out of the twenty-four hours. I wouldn't be able to go through that any more. I had a reeling, a *méagram,* in my head from her.'

'Well, now,' says the woman, 'I have a proposition myself and you mightn't find any fault with it. Bend down you head.'

And she whispered to him for there were some people in the shop, and she told him about Nell Casey, and if you were there and watching his countenance you could see that he was taking the bait. When she finished he said:

'I'll be in again at the end of the week.'

He was in the following morning! An account of a

match was sent to Casey's, and there was no trouble whatever in making it. Jeremiah bought a very expensive wedding ring for her. Indeed he was so delighted that Nell couldn't talk, if he could have afforded it at all he'd nearly have bought the lakes of Killarney and the hills of Connemara for her.

We'll skip now till the night of the wedding. No shortage of anything. Plenty of food and drink, and out in the night when they had enough of the Highland Fling and the Kerry Victoria, enough singing and reciting, a lot of the lads there had a good cargo on board, and one of them suggested why not play the game called 'Kick the Turnip', which was common in that quarter. And how the game was played was, you'd get a sizeable turnip and cut a channel around the equator. You'd tie a rope into that and at the other end of the rope you'd put a similar weight, maybe another turnip. You'd throw it over the collar-brace and then you could adjust the turnip up or down, a foot from the ground or whatever you wanted. And the man that'd win the game 'd be the man that'd tip the turnip with the top of his toecap and it the highest from the ground.

They put it a few feet from the floor first, so as to give old lads a chance. There were some men there could kick the turnip and it on one level with their chins, and more couldn't touch it and it only up to their navels. Then someone said, 'What about Jeremiah O'Sullivan the man of the moment. Would he have a go!'

'Faith,' Jeremiah said, 'I will have a go. Why not!'

He was out to show off his agility in front of his young wife, and the people. He went down to the butt of the kitchen and buttoning his coat, he gave

'Kick the Turnip'

instructions to put the turnip five foot four from the floor, and running up he met the turnip with the father and mother of an almighty kick, and sent it spinning around the collar brace, but with the dint of exertion, the other leg was taken from under him and he came down with a slap on the floor, his poll hopped off the flag, making a loud report, and he went out like a light. his face as pale as the candle.

They began splashing water on him to revive him. His wife Nell was over at the fire preparing some grudles, and turning around, when she saw her husband that she only married that day out for the count, her mouth opened wide and a gush of speech came out. She ran over saying:

'Jeremiah, Jeremiah, Oh my darling Jeremiah, open your mouth, Jeremiah, and tell me you are not dead!'

Jeremiah opened one eye a small bit and said to the crowd:

'If that's my second wife talking, don't throw any more water on me, I'd rather be dead!'

He didn't die at all, and he got on fairly well with Nell. He was as happy with her as he was with the other one, for a while anyway. One in family is all they had. Yerra, the man was old. Eighteen or nineteen years older than the girl. For God's sake! Where would you be going without a bell on your bike! Nell was young and lively, she used be going around to all the house dances, where she'd be out in the floor in every set, as as time went by Jeremiah found he did not have the wherewithal to keep up the tally. Younger men'd ask her out dancing — you couldn't blame Nell for going out with 'em, and Jeremiah got jealous and jealousy is the worst thing that ever took a seat in the human heart.

Blackguards took advantage of this, and they were

saying things in his hearing and Jeremiah was reading his own meaning into everything he heard. They'd say:

'Did you hear about the man that used be away from home. It would be three weeks before he'd get back to wind the clock. Well, himself and the wife went to confession. She was inside and he was outside waiting to go in, and in the middle of her story she opened the door of the box and said to the husband:

"Jim, when you were away from home last month, can you remember how many days did I say the carpenter was in making the press?"

The thing about that story was that Jeremiah used to truck a bit in cattle, he'd often be away from home for three nights at a time, which gave the imagination plenty of scope to expand. One morning the children were gone to school, two he had, one by the first wife and one by the second, and Nell was gone binding to the Callaghan's. There alone in the kitchen jealousy got such a hold of him that he took a crock off the dresser, filled it with fresh cream and going down in the room positioned it centre ways under the bed. Then he took the pendulum off the clock, it was stopped anyway, and attached it underneath to the spring of the bed, adjusting it in such a way that the pendulum would not touch the cream with only Nell in the bed! And how he judged Nell's weight was with a half sack of Reliable flour. Now that the trap was set he went off driving cattle down to Charleville.

When he came back in a few days' time he went straight down in the room and took the crock from under the bed. He looked into it. There was butter in it!

The way a man can be fooled. He was grinding his teeth with the dint of bad stuff. What he wouldn't say and what he wouldn't do to Nell. He ran out in the yard in a fit of temper and remained outside until the children came in from school; there was no trace of Nell. He had occasion to come in for the donkey's winkers, below in the room they used to keep the tackling, and when he went down there was his daughter by the first wife, a big mopsey of a one that should have sense, and his little girl by Nell and they dancing up and down on the bed.

'Taney tip and taney tow,
Turn the ship and away we go!'

THE EFFIGY

Some people'd keep an all night vigil at the holy well. They'd pay the first round at nightfall and then sit by the well praying through the dark, or crowd inside the ruin, where they'd light a fire, until it was time to pay the second round at dawn. These'd mostly be the afflicted. You'd see a mother there with a sick child hoping for a cure and she calling out to the patron saint:

'Is chugatsa a thánag ag gearán mo scéil leat,
Is d'iarraidh mo leighis ar son Dé ort!'[1]

And in Kilfinora they'd keep a vigil for nine nights and the women'd bring their beds, and when the beds were set up around the holy well, with the hawkers' tents below and the fun of the fair at the side, you wouldn't see the like of it in Tibet. At nightfall the quilts 'd be lifted up and tied to the four brass knobs to make a roof over the bed to keep out the dew, and around dawn you'd see these draperies being pulled aside and the women putting their heads out to see was there enough light to commence the first round.

And they tell of a woman that woke a bit late the ninth morning. She was so upset at having missed the round at dawn that in her excitement to get to her crutches, that were a bit away from her, she walked! She wasn't the only one. There was this man paralysed in the bones dragging himself from station to station

41

and on the ninth morning he shouted out that someone touched him on the knee.

'Keep out from me,' he said, ''tis the sorest part of my body!'

Jacko McGann who was a witness to it, told me that no one went near him. Jacko said he heard something no louder than the flutter of a bird's wing and saw, what he could only describe as a human outline bend down and touch the suffering man on the knee. And Jacko went over to him and said:

'Get up out of it!'

And he said the man got up and he walked!

At the twelfth station in Carraig an Adhmaid, which is the priest's tomb, you come to the effigy on the keystone so high up you'd pass it ten times a day without noticing it. To get to it you'd stand on the sill inside the ruin and reach out through the window and up and the figure is so small you'd cover it with the palm of your hand. Under your fingers you could make out the little monkey face and the neck. It had no clothes on, and the two hands came down to cover its nakedness. You rubbed your handkerchief to it making the sign of the Cross. You'd step down then into the ruin, where you'd see the sign of the fire after the vigil of the night before, and there'd be a travelling man there breaking a stone into small pieces and he'd give you a bit for a penny. You'd tie that scrap of slaty stone in a knot in your handkerchief and you'd keep it for luck.

But the naked figure reminds me of Ned Connor. Ned was a young lad of seventeen or eighteen years of age and he had a fierce row with his father. Ned wanted the price of a new suit of clothes, because he couldn't go outside the door in the old duds, and the father refused to give him the money. Ned lost his temper and said to his father:

'Wouldn't you even give me the price of a new cap, so that I can put my head out the window itself?'

The father wouldn't part with the money and God knows Ned was working hard enough for him.

'Alright so,' the son said, 'you'll never again lay an eye on me.' He ran away in the middle of the night in the general direction of America, and in the morning he came to Cromane pier and jumping into a small boat he hit the fisherman on the back and said:

'Boston, *a bhuachaill!*'

When it was explained to him that Boston was three thousand miles away and that no one had made the journey in a small boat since Saint Brendan discovered America, he said:

'What'll I do so? I promised my father last night that he'd never see me again.'

'Go away into Tralee,' says the fisherman, 'and join the Munster Fusiliers and if you do, ten chances to one but he'll never see you again.'

Ned Connor went into Tralee and joined the Munster Fusiliers. He was put into a new uniform and when he got his first week's pay he went down the town and into a public house, and even though he had no experience of drink, yet he lowered pint for pint with hardened old campaigners back from Khartoum. And when at closing time he came out in the street and hit the fresh air he was legless, stocious! He went down through the town singing and missed the turn to Ballymullen Barracks, and kept on taking the two sides of the road out into the country towards Castleisland. When the pins got tired under him he sat on a mossy bank at the side of the road, and he was so befuddled in his mind that he thought he was sitting on the edge of his bed in the barracks, so he kicked off the shoes;

took off his little military hat; took off every single stitch, and folding up his tunic and trousers like he was shown to do by the officer, he put them, as he thought, under the bed! Where did he shove 'em only down a gullet at the side of the road, and standing there in his pelt he gave a blast of one of the Munsters' songs:

'Tell my brothers when you go home
How nobly I fought and died.
With a bayonet hanging by my breast,
And a small sword by my side,
Tell them at home that I'll ne'r more roam
As I did in my boyhood days,
Where the grass never fades
In the pleasant cool shades
Of old Ireland far away!'

He lay down then on the mossy bank and went to sleep, but there is one thing I must tell ye, no matter how high the alcoholic content in the blood, the frost will overcome it! The cold went into the marrow of his bones, and he woke up and walked away rubbing his eyes. He didn't even know that he was naked! A call of nature that drew his attention to it! He had to keep walking for he was frozen to a frazzle. As he came round a turn he saw a light a bit in from the road. He went into the yard and threw a stone at the door. 'Twas as near as he could go to it in his condition. A young woman appeared so he ducked down behind the hedge, nothing up but the head, that was all right, and she said:

'Won't you come in!'

'I can't go in,' he said, 'I am standing here as naked as when I came into the world.'

'Well,' says she, 'there's a suit of clothes here that'll never be used again.' And she went into the house and

...nothing up but the head, that was all right,...

threw him out the clothes and shut the door — very considerate. He went up and he got into the trousers first. And even though that trousers was too big for him, he could put two more into it with himself, it was like heaven to be inside in it for every limb of his body was in an icicle. He put on the shirt, waistcoat and coat, the socks, shoes and hat, and he went into the house. She put him sitting at the fire and filled him out a full cup of poteen, and went off up in the room with the bottle.

When you come into a house like that out of the dark it takes a bit of time for you to get accustomed to the light. He was taking stock of his surroundings and looking over towards the dresser — the Lord save us, he saw a corpse laid out on the settle. An old man, his hands joined and the rosary beads entwined around his knuckes, and the butt of a blessed candle lighting on the shelf above him.

Ned got an awful fright and he ran up in the room, and God knows he got a bigger fright when he went up. There was the young woman of the house above, sitting on another man's knee and she pouring drink into him, whatever was the meaning of it. He came back down and said:

'I must have some bit of religion in me.'

He knelt down to say his prayers. And like at a wake when you are praying you are looking at the corpse's face, and after a while a tiny spider came down on his rope, had a look at the lie of the land, and then alighted on the cheek bone. Wasn't it narrow the world was on him! The little spider rubbed some of his legs together and after another bit of fidgeting, skirted a tuft of hair that was growing there and walked into the furrow below the eye towards the bridge of the dead man's nose. Then Ned's heart came up in his

46

mouth for he saw the eye twitching. He made a dart to go, but if he did the corpse put out his hand and caught him, saying:

'Don't move, or if you do, *corp'on diabhal*, I'll kill you. I had to do this,' he said, 'I am an old man married to a young wife, I had to let on to be dead to catch her out. I've caught her out now. You go down to the *cúl-lochta* and bring me up the three prong pike!'

Ned went down, brought up the pike and lifting the sheet put it by the 'corpse' in the bed.

'Go up now in the room,' says the old man, 'and turn down my wife and Jack the Cuckoo!'

The soldier went up to the door and said:

'Ye're wanting!'

The two came down and as they crossed the kitchen the 'corpse' hopped out of the bed, and as they went through the front door Jack the Cuckoo got a damn fine dart of the three prongs of the pike in the backside. That knocked the gimp off him! He wasn't able to sit down until Christmas!

'Take that going!' says the old man, and says he to his wife, 'never let me see your face again!' And he slapped out the door and said to the soldier:

'You can stay the night and keep the clothes. If I was dead in earnest she'd have given 'em to some poor man to wear three Sundays to Mass.'

In the morning the soldier didn't know how he was going to face the barracks in Tralee in those old clothes. He made another sally back to see if he could find the place he slept the night before. No. No good, there was no trace of the uniform, and as the morning was going he decided to cut across the nearway to Tralee. There were horny sheep in the field alongside the road, and as Ned walked by, a ram feeding there lifted his head, and when he saw the loose backside to

47

Ned's trousers, a sure sign of a blackguard, the ram shook himself and like a bullet out of a gun he charged after the soldier giving him a dunt that threw him out on his face and eyes.

Ned Connor got up only to find that the ram was settling himself for another charge. Well there was nothing for it, only catch him by the horns, and he did and knocked the ram back on his rump. Then the thought struck him, looking at the distance between him and the ditch, that he couldn't afford to let the ram go anymore, he was sore enough!

Well, as luck 'd have it who came down the road but an R.I.C. man and Ned asked him to hold the ram while he was going over the ditch for a rope to tie him. The policeman came in and as he caught the ram by the horns, he said:

'Is he cross?'

And Ned said, 'Like a lamb, eroo!'

The soldier went off, by the way to get the rope, and when he got over the ditch he ducked down and ran like hell for Tralee. The policeman was left there so-hoing the ram, and every now and then he'd call over the ditch to see if Ned was coming back with the rope. Finally he got sick of it saying: 'Ah! Here he's poor enough to be his own servant.' He let the ram go and walked away. Merciful hour! The dunt he got! That was another man that didn't sit down until Christmas!

In the barrack square in Tralee the sergeant major was drilling a squad of the Munster Fusiliers and giving 'em dog's abuse.

'Left, left! ye're in the army now,
Lift 'em up! ye're not behind the plough,
Ye're not going to get rich digging a ditch,
Ye're in the army now!'

48

He numbered them off, formed 'em into fours and gave them their marching orders:

'By the left quick march!'

They went off and just then the sergeant major looked and who was coming in the gate but Ned Connor in the big suit. The sleeves down over his hands and the hat down over his eyes. The sergeant major when he saw the *geatch* of him got such a hearty fit of laughing he forgot to halt the soldiers! They were half way up to the Councy Limerick before an officer on horseback got up to 'em.

Ned got thirty days C.B. for losing the Queen's uniform — Queen Victoria that was there at the time, she'd look sweet in it! And he was only barely out of quad when he was put on board ship for South Africa. The Boer war had broken out. Ned used to write home to the mother, he never forgave the father for not giving him the suit. The mother used to read the letters for the post boy because the post boy was in the same book as Ned going to school, and he'd like to know how he was getting on in Africa. In one letter Ned said:

'Well, Mom, we're up to our eyes in it now, last night we made another shift for Ladysmith!'

'Look at that' says the mother, 'isn't the army great training for 'em, when he was at home he couldn't sew in a button!'

They used to say that time that one of the Munsters in a letter home to his father said: 'The army is a hoor! Sell the pig and buy me out!' And that the father wrote back saying, 'Sorry for your trouble son. We killed the pig, soldier on!'

Ned didn't see much service in South Africa. He was invalided out of it. He got kicked by a mule in the Transvaal — a bloody sore thing too! He came home on a small pension and I'll never forget years after

49

hearing Ned one night at a pattern at Carraig an Adhmaid. Now, my neighbours, who were there, could spend the whole night talking about animals, and the ways of animals ... the fox with the sweet tooth and the clever way he goes about robbing a wild honey bee's nest. They were curious about the four-footed inhabitants of South Africa, and asked Ned what they were like. Well, Ned described the animals he saw to us, and I don't think the like of 'em were ever on the face of the earth! He said the biggest quadruped he saw there, it must be the elephant he was talking about, was a huge, bulging affair, like a gutteperka bull, picking up grass with his tail and shoving it up in his arse!

And he told us that himself and Danielo Moran, he was from Áthnablátha, were on scout patrol along the edge of the jungle on the look out for Boers. They came to a hole in an embankment and Danielo, who was of a curious turn of mind, went in, and where was he but in a lion's den. He came out and told Ned, that there were lovely cubs inside, and that he'd love to catch two of 'em, and bring back to the bivouac and maybe when the war'd be over he could bring 'em home to Ireland.

'Dammit,' he said, 'when they'd grow up you could put 'em ploughing!'

He told Ned to watch out for the big lion in case he came back while Danielo was in the den. Ned standing on sentry outside put a bit in the pipe, and when he went to light it there was a breeze blowing, so he turned sideways and when he turned back the lion was half way in the hole! He had to do something quick, so he caught him by the tail, and as Ned explained to us, if we knew anything about zoology, there's a fierce knob at the end of a lion's tail. This gave him a great grip and he held on for all he was worth putting his two shoes at either side of the hole. Danielo, the man inside, noticed that something was wrong and he shouted out:

'Ned, what's darkening the hole?'

'By jamonies,' says Ned, 'if the tail breaks you'll soon know what's darkening it!'

To save the man's life inside, Ned, with great presence of mind, drew his revolver and shot the lion. I'm too much of a gentleman to tell ye where he shot him. Mercy of God, he didn't shoot the other man in the head coming out. Danielo managed to commandeer two cubs and brought 'em to the place where they were bivouaced. Himself and Ned put 'em on the bottle like two neddy bonavs. Well, they were the talk of South Africa with the two cubs walking around after 'em. When Queen Victoria got a wrinkle of it she sent out her special man for the cubs and they were the first lions to come to the London Zoo!

1. It's to you I came with the story of my complaint
And I asked you to cure me for God's sake.

ABBEY'S BOWL

There were curing stones that time at the holy well, you'd see 'em glistening in the sun after a shower of rain. They'd be about as big as a goose egg, and you could rub one of them into yourself wherever you felt the greatest need for it, or you could rub your rosary beads, or a holy medal to it, and continue the treatment when you came home. In one place in Ireland there was a relic. I heard a man describe it as something in the nature of a knuckle-bone, or an ankle bone. It was a human bone, I suppose a saint's bone, and it was kept at arm's length in a secret place in the wall, and if you were so bad in bed that you couldn't get up, that relic could be brought to the house to you. There was such great faith in these healing objects at the time that a young girl over in America, and not getting a day of her health there, expressed a wish to have the relic brought out to her. It was her own cousin Thade Nóin brought out the relic baked inside in a cake of bread. She applied it for nine mornings running, without a bite going inside her lips, and she was game ball after it! She married a fine handsome man. He wasn't from Ireland now he was from Italy. Then it was her brother John, coming home on a trip, that brought the relic back to Ireland concealed inside a victrolla, what the returning Yanks called the first gramaphones that came to Ireland. The ones with the funnel out at the side. They used to have these records that were there at the time:

'Shake hands with your Uncle Dan, me boys,
And this is your cousin Kate,
She's the girl you used to swing
Down by the Garden gate.
Shake hands with all the neighbours
And kiss the colleens all!
You're as welcome as the flowers in May
If you never came at all!'

John's concern was not how he was going to bring the relic into Ireland, but how would he tell his mother that her daughter had married an Italian in New York. At that time, I don't know what they are like now, certain old ladies would take a poor view of that message. This is the tune you'd hear from 'em:

'What did you say his name was again?'
'Lord save us! What's wrong with Irish boys!'

So when the welcoming was over in the kitchen, John decided to take the bull by the horns and he said:
'Say, Mom, I suppose you heard that Mary got buckled?'
And the mother said, 'We got a wrinkle of it. What's the boy like?'
'A fine handsome man!'
'Where's he from?' says Mother.
And the son to knock the sting out of it said:
'He's from the Pope's place!'
That was all right.
Some of those curing stones you would not bring 'em to America unless you wanted to rub 'em to a

53

buffalo, for they were for curing animals. And such a thing was Abbey's Bowl so called because it was similar in shape and size to the thing they have for bowl playing. There was also Abbey's cord and if your mother wore that around herself the night before you were born, your first journey, as dangerous as any one you'll ever undertake again, could prove an uneventful passage! You'll find Abbey's Bowl at arms length in a square hole in the wall over at Carraig an Adhmaid and when I was small I was told that it was in suspense, not touching the wall anywhere, and you could take it out and bring it to the house if a cow had timber tongue, dry murrain or black quarter. One man was going for it so often, when he finished rubbing it to the cow he threw it on top of the dresser and forgot all about it. The wife whitewashing for the stations found the holy object and made him put it back in its proper place. Then the next time he went for it he couldn't bring it out over the stream. There was like an invisible wall in front of him. Cold sweat came out through him as he tried to push his way across the bridge. There was a donkey grazing there and he went spread legs on him, but when the animal came up his head went skeeting along the 'glass' wall. Then he put the bowl up on the parapet of the bridge. It was the time the penny-farthing bicycle was invented, and he went down to the village, borrowed a bike, put the bowl in his pocket, hopped on the bike and came flying out over the bridge with it. The saints have no power over machinery! That curing stone is cemented into the wall now, and I think that's because two of the boys on the run the time of the trouble, took it out and went bowl playing with it. Didn't the same two take the water out of the holy well and bring it to a house and put it down boiling in the kettle and made tea with it!

54

A RUMINATING ANIMAL

Talking about curing animals, there was a time in Ireland when those living in the congested districts knew as much about a horse as a dog knows about a holiday. At that time the country was teeming with people. They got married young and to give 'em a living the farms had to be divided and sub-divided until before the famine a whole family'd be existing on less than an acre of ground. They'd turn the sod with the spade, stick the *skiollawns* and bring out the dung in a *cliabh* on their back from the yard. What did they want a horse for! He'd be only coming in their way. Another mouth to feed! If they went away down to the main road they might see a landlord passing with a horse and some of those had more than one.

At that time there were these two brothers and they fell in for an *ábhar* of money and nothing in the wide world'd do 'em but to get a horse, *éirí in airde gan cur leis!* They made off Cahirmee fair and they bought a tried animal and they brought him home. When they were coming near their own place the people were taking the legs of one another running to the door when they saw the horse passing. They were shouting after the brothers and saying:

'What do he ate and do he bellow?'

They brought the horse into their own yard, they had no stable. Yerra, there was next to nothing in the line of out offices going with houses at that time, for the more out offices you had the more rent you'd pay to the landlord. So they brought the horse into the kitchen and down in the room, indeed they thought so highly of him, if they could have managed it at all, they'd nearly have put him into the bed! The kitchen was full of people, only very near neighbours and relations left in to view the horse at close quarters. And when they got an eyeful of him they were all put out for it was near his feeding time. The brothers had their instructions from the man they bought the horse from in Cahirmee, and the first item on the horse's menu was a tub of water tepid, followed up with a few *dorns* of oats in the bottom of a pan. They knew about putting the bag on his head but they didn't want to do this the first night in case the mother'd think they were going playing blind man's buff with him. And the final course was a gabhal of Italian ryegrass. Then the two brothers put their shoulders to the jambs of the room door watching every single bite that went into the horse's mouth. You'd think they were eating it themselves, the way their jaws'd move in time with the horse's chewing, until finally the father sitting by the fire said:

'Can't ye close down the door and give the animal some privacy!' They came and sat by the fire and in a while's time one of the brothers went down to see how the horse was getting on and the father shouted down after him:

'Did he finish what was in front of him?'

The son said, 'He did.'

'What's he doing now?'

And the son said, 'Nothing.'

'Did he lie down?'

'No!'

56

...watching every single bite that went into the horse's mouth.

Oh this was bad. The old man came running down and the horse was standing firm on three legs, the right hind leg half drawn up to him with the toe of the hoof on the ground, for all the world like a step dancer waiting for a hole in the music! The horse was nodding and his eyes were half shut. Of course what those poor people didn't know was, a horse can sleep standing up like a civil servant!

The old man felt the tops of his ears. If they are cold its a good sign, and he ran his hand over the horse's nose to see would he feel the little *drúcteens* of sweat — a wet nose and dry somewhere else is a healthy sign of an animal. *Mo léir cráite,* the horse had a moustache on him like a drum-major! They get that from munching furze, which can be taken as a hint if there's anyone having difficulty in growing a moustache. Nothing would convince those people but that the horse was sick. They were looking a his loose mouth and when he'd go 'brrrrah' they thought he was trying to throw up!

'Maybe he was overlooked,' the mother said, 'and it wouldn't put a blister on anyone's tongue to say 'God bless the animal!'

They sat around the fire and at six o'clock in the morning when the horse wasn't lying down or acting in a normal fashion according to their lights, one of the sons was sent for the curing stone to the holy well. On his way home he met that little ex-soldier that was stopping at Dinny's at the time — he used to be in charge of horses at Lord Headley's — and he said to the son:

'Why are you out so early?'

'We've sickness in the house,' he said.

'Is it your father?'

'No,' the son said, 'it is the horse.'

The ex-soldier came up to the house and went down in the room and opened the horse's mouth and looked into it, lifted the lid to see was the eye bloodshot, he looked in his frog and examined every detail; he lifted up his tail fairly high to see how it would fall. Then he slapped him on the rump saying:

'Wee, hoa, hack, stand up, stand up there!'

This woke the animal and he shook his head showing the white of his eye, which is a healthy sign of a horse or a woman. The ex-soldier began to laugh.

'There's nothing wrong with him,' he said, 'he's as healthy as myself.'

'Are you blind?' says the father, 'or what sort of an expert are you? Can't you see he is not chewing the cud!'

DUGGAN'S FIELD

The day of the pattern in Duggan's field the young people'd be dancing on the grass, Tom Billy playing for 'em. No matter how you pounded on the field you'd make no sound which meant the music was much clearer.

'I have a bonnet trimmed with blue.
Why don't you wear it, sure I do.
Why don't you wear it when you can,
Going to the dance with your young man.
Dah dil doh dil ditty doh . . .'

That'd be the signal for the young men to put their hands around the young women and pull 'em into 'em. Dah dil doh dil ditty doh. They were off on another round moving with sun. Dah dil doh dil ditty doh.

'Are you one of the Donovan's? I'd know you out of your Auntie Bridgie. Any chance of the convey? Have you a sister? I have why so. There's a fellow with me.'

Some young men had no mind for dancing. They'd be in another corner weight lifting — plenty rocks there for it. Or putting the shot. They'd select a round stone — it would give you enough to do to hold it up. And you'd see them swivelling it in the palm of their hand to get a good grip. Then with a wild burst of energy they'd go tearing up to the *teip* and let go. No follow through, that could disqualify you. Or they'd be jumping, the high jump, the long jump and the hop, step and lep. Or they might be fencing. This was in imitation of the quality except that the quality had swords. Blackthorn sticks these men had, for in olden days the plain people of Ireland were forbidden to carry arms — I tell you they made up for it since!

These were the same blackthorn sticks that were used in the faction fights when the Lynch's and the Twomey's went in for a bit of skull cracking below in Maybury's lawn. Every young man'd have his Sunday suit on coming to the pattern, and the object of the 'sword' fight was to knock the buttons out of the other fellow's coat, and his job was, by thrust and by parry, to keep you out from him, and the man that'd lose the fight 'd be the man that couldn't button his coat going home. That mightn't bother him if he had the convey!

There'd be so many young girls at the City. They'd be there from over the hill and from all quarters, their saintly faces half hidden in their shawls as they prayed by the well. You'd never think then that the bulk of those young women would consider it a day wasted if they hadn't the company of a young man going home that night. There'd be so much conveying, especially if the pattern was held in the summer time, that in the morning the farmers'd be on the points of going to the presbytery to complain — acres of grass corn flattened!

In another part of the field you'd have lads too old for dancing, too old for weight lifting, and God help us, too old for flattening grass corn, but if they had a sup in they were damn fine singers, and they could put a good face to a story. Those men knew the history of the holy well and they admitted that despite the piety of the people in the morning when night fell the commandments came in for a fair hammering. There

These were the same sticks that were used in the faction fights...

was an amount of drinking that time, and courting, and fighting, and women! If the pattern was within walking distance of a port town or a city, women putting themselves in the way of earning a penny would come to it. Many is the man found himself without his watch and chain after a whirl!

But there was only one thing that would desecrate the holy well and that was the taking of life. A man was killed the evening of a pattern and no one knew who his murderer was. During the weeks that followed a woman was paying rounds at the well and she was getting no relief from her ailment. She took a crock of the spring to a man that knew more than his prayers. He blew on it and the water in the crock turned into blood!

'The Lord save us!' the woman said, 'what does that signify?'

And he said: 'A man with blood on his hands washed himself in the holy well.'

She wondered who it could be and the man made a circle on the ground and built a fire around the rim of it, for all the world like the fire the smith used to make for reddening the iron band for a cart wheel. When the fire was lit he put the crock in the middle.

'Look through the smoke,' he said to the woman. She did, and in the circle she saw the outline of a young man and he was her own son. The well would not be the same until the murderer was brought to book for his crime, and how you'd know the well was restored, you'd see the little trout swimming in it. Then the priest would be asked to bless it. He would be only too glad to come, although I never saw a priest doing the rounds at the holy well. I don't think they believed in it, for no one could accept all the things that were said about the well.

THE MERMAID

As ye all know I'm a stonemason by trade and it is behind in Ballinskelligs I was one time building a pier. Tough enough work too, and you'd want to be well paid for it. And in a job like that, down on the brink of the tide, there are times when the shoes'd have to come off. Well, one day I noticed that the man tending me had webbed toes and of course I remarked on it. But it wasn't until that night above in Main's pub that I came by the whole story.

'You remarked on a certain thing down at the pier today, Ned,' says the man sitting beside me in the snug.

'That I did,' says I, 'if you are alluding to the lad of the webbed toes'.

'The very man,' says he, 'a boy of the Shea's. Did you ever hear, Ned, that the Shea's are descended from the mermaid?'

'Never!' says I. 'Have you the running of it?'

'I have,' says he, 'and it isn't belittling anyone of the name I am for I'm a Shea man myself. The old stock and rooted in this quarter since before history began.'

'You're losing track of the mermaids,' says I.

'I'm not,' he said, and I knew by the way he settled himself that we were in for a night of it.

64

'The first Shea man,' says he, 'that came to this quarter had no wife, and it is said that he was taking the air down by the sea this day when the mermaids came up out of the ocean, and after a time they went back into the ocean, all except one. And what did this one do but come out of the black thing they have covering theirself from the elbows down. It is like a one-legged trousers with a fish tail at the end of it. And there she stood as lovely a young girl as you could wish to see!

'She threw the fish tail up on the black rock and went for a canter down along the strand. Back she came again, got into the fish tail and hit off out into the ocean. The Shea man didn't sleep a wink that night only thinking of her, and the sun wasn't far up in the heavens the next day when he was down by the sea again. He waited and the mermaids came and she came and the performance was the same as the day before.

'Well, the more he saw her the more he felt she was the only woman for him, for to give her only her due she was pure beautiful. He watched her antics for a week and then he hit on a plan, for as the man said: "Faint heart never won fair lady".

'So this day he hid near the black rock and when she was gone for her canter down along the strand he whipped the fish tail and made off. She went after him and implored of him to give it back to her, that without the fish tail she could not make her way back through the sea to her own people. He told her of his fine farm of land and a house all to himself.

"And don't you think," says he, "that you'd be a lot better off sitting down in front of a roaring fire in my place than to be getting your death in a damp oul cave!"

65

'He kept before her to the house and when he had her in the kitchen he shut the door on her and kept her inside. They were married in a few days — letters of freedom and all this coming and going that's in the world today was not necessary in those days. They were happy out together and in time the children were rising to 'em, and even though they had no secrets from one another in the style of all true lovers, there was one thing she never found out, and that was where he hid the fish tail. Times she would ask him for it, and those times he would pretend to be deaf, for he knew that if she got it she'd go back to the sea to her own people and they'd keep her from him.

'As I said the children were rising to 'em and they were no more than able to crawl when the mother would bring 'em every day down to the black rock where she'd sit looking out to sea. When the eldest lad was crabbed enough she told him to keep an eye on his father, and if he ever saw him with a black thing like a fish tail to come and tell her.

'Faith, she put her commission in the right hands, for that little lad was so sharp he'd nearly see a midge winking on top of a tall chimney. That was in the fall of the year and the Shea man had the oats in the haggard waiting to be threshed. And far back as that time was they had threshing machines. Engines were not invented, but the drum was turned by having a horse running around in a circle. If my memory serves me hadn't they the same plan for making butter. Now, when oats was threshed there were three things you could do with it that time; you could bag it, put it in the loft or put it in a *sheegogue*. And what was that? Well, I'll tell you — it was a straw granary.

'You'd make a *sugawn,* three to six inches thick. Begin by making a circle, say eight feet in diameter on

66

a stone platform in the haggard. Keep coiling the straw rope on that circle and throwing the grain into the middle as you went along, until you ended up with what looked like an enormous straw barrel, the sides splaying out so that it was much wider at the top. When the *sheegogue* was a little over the height of a man and filled with grain, you'd put a cone-shaped roof of straw on it. Thatch that roof with rushes, leaving a good eve all round, and your grain was secure for the winter.

'The men were in Shea's haggard threshing and the Shea man was in one corner putting the grain in the *sheegogue*. The eldest son was there too, his eyes on *kippens*, and after a time he ran in and told his mother that he saw his father putting a black thing like a fish tail under the grain in the new *sheegogue*. The mother didn't say, 'yes', 'aye' or 'no', but went on preparing the supper for the men that would be coming in from the haggard bye an' bye. After the supper the neighbouring girls came to the house and there was a dance, and the Shea woman was as happy as anyone there, out on the floor in every set. She was only known to laugh three times since she came to this life, she laughed the night of her wedding, she laughed when her first child spoke and she was laughing tonight.

'Around eleven o'clock the dance broke up and everyone went home satisfied after a most enjoyable night. Came the morning and the Shea man nudged his elbow out from him.

"Hop out woman! The day'll be gone!"

'*Mo léir*, he was alone in the hammock. He got up then and he called her, and he called the children to go out there looking for their mother. He went out himself and the fowl house door was open but the fowl were not in the yard. It was the geese gave the game away for he heard them noising in the haggard. He ran up that way, and there was the bottom *sugawn* pulled out from under the *sheegogue* with the grain spilling out and the geese gobbling it up.

'He knew then what had happened. He knew then that she was gone from him, back to the sea and to her own people and that he'd never lay an eye on her again. And he threw himself against the side of the *sheegogue* for the weight of the world was on him.

'It was there the children found him. And those children missed their mother, but as was their custom, when she was with 'em, they'd go every day to the black rock, where they'd find every sort of fish left out for 'em. She never saw 'em short and they grew up to be fine handsome men and women, and they had the webbed toes you'll find on their descendents down to this present day.' That's the story now as I heard it that night in the snug of Main's Public House in Ballinskelligs.

MINDING THE HOUSE

Oh Carrig an Adhmaid! Oh Cathair Chrobh Dhearg! If you fell in with the right company in either place the night of the pattern you would hear talk!

There was this woman and her husband was always finding fault with her work around the house. A snout on him looking into the pots and pans watching what she was doing.

Finally she lost her patience.

'Look, we'll change places tomorrow,' says she, 'let you remain inside minding the house and I'll go setting *skiollawns*.' It was in the springtime. In the morning after milking the cows she took the spade and hit for the field, not before she specified her husband's duties for the day. He was to turn out the *braddy* cow for a drink around eleven; he was to feed the calves and to feed the fowl; he was to bake a cake; he was to iron his shirt; make the churn, and go to the well. And most important of all he was to keep his eye on the goose hatching in the big box below the dresser. I think it's twenty-eight days for a goose! The goslings were due out any minute and it would be a calamity if the goose got off the eggs. And he was to have her dinner on the table for her when she'd come in at one o'clock on the dot.

She went off and left him inside and there was no more awkward man from here to Kildimo, but isn't it the likes of him that'd criticize. The first thing he did was to sit down, and map out a plan of campaign, for as he said that's what was wrong with women—no plan!

'Now,' he said, 'so as to have the fire free later on for to cook the dinner, I'll bake the cake now, and at the same time heat the iron to iron my shirt.'

He put the iron to the fire and spilled the makings of the cake into the *lasaid,* added salt, and bread soda and began tossing it up and down. He was flour to the eyebrows. From rubbing his hands to his face and searching his pockets for his pipe, he finished up as white as if you pulled him through a lime kiln! He made a hole in the middle of the flour and poured in sour milk, mixing the whole thing and kneading it into dough. And of course he made it too wet; there was more dough on his hands than there was in the *lasaid*. Then he got the oven. He didn't bother putting it over the fire to heat it, or he didn't shake a dust of flour on the bottom or around the sides to keep the cake from tying to it. No. He just got the dough off his hands and lobbed it in one big lump into the oven. He never put the sign of the cross or anything on it with the knife; hung the oven over the fire; put on the lid, and put the live coals on top of it. That was one job done.

He took up the iron now and to see if it was hot he put it to his cheek. It isn't hot it was but red. He proceeded to iron the shirt, and for this operation he had a huge audience. Hens along the half door, calves looking in through the window, all with their mouths open complaining, for he had forgotten to feed 'em.

The noise was deafening and he went to prepare a collation for 'em, forgetting of course to put the iron on an upside-down saucer, when he came back there was a fine black triangle burned down through the shirt and half way through the table! He had to throw his hat with that for a bad job.

He decided now to make the churn, and go to the well.

It was a timber churn, what was known as a dash-churn, and the churn was made by hitting a staff up and down inside it. He took the staff out, that was a bit old fashioned for him. Then he spilled a tub of cream into the churn and put on the cover, and so as to be able to do two jobs at the one time — make the churn and go for water — he took the reins off the donkey's winkers and tied the churn on his back. That left his two hands free to pick up two buckets, and he said, with the movement of his body while he was walking to the well, the churn'd be making! What woman'd think of that!

Now, the well was deep and when he bent down to fill the bucket the end of the churn went up, the cover fell off and the cream shot out over his head and ran down inside his shirt like lava down the side of Vesuvius. As he walked back with the buckets he was kicking cream out of the legs of his trousers. But that was nothing to the confusion that was in the house before him.

He left the doors open going out. The calves were above in the room, the hens up on the dresser, the cock inside in the press, the dog making love to the bacon, and the cat with his head down to the two shoulders inside in the jug of milk. The cat couldn't get his head out of the jug. 'A chait, out of that,' the man said. And the cat hopped off the table and made flitters of the jug on the floor, giving himself such a fright that he went out the door spitting! The man had to go then and turn the calves down out of the room and the cock and the hens out of the press:

'Out blast ye, out! hurrish! Suck out of that!'

71

He turned 'em all out into the yard but before he could do another thing, he was so uncomfortable with the cream down inside his shirt, he had to take all his clothes off and go out and roll in the grass to dry himself. He came in then sops hanging out of him. The burned shirt was nearest to his hand so he put that on, but before he had time to go in the room to put on his trousers he noticed that in his excitement, when he was turning out the other animals, he turned out the goose as well.

'If the goose got off the eggs it would be a calamity!' the wife had warned him. He went over and put his hand on the eggs and they were cold. He went to the door and called the goose.

'*Badaoi, badaoi, badaoi!*'

There was no trace of badaoi.

'What will I do now,' he said, 'the goslings could be dying in the shells at this moment. What will she say to me when she comes in!' He thought to himself that the heat of his own body might approximate that of the goose, so he went down and sat over the eggs. He couldn't put his weight on 'em, the weight had to be transferred to the two shins. And there he was when Moll Simon, a neighbouring girl, put her head in the door.

Moll was well into years, a girl that never settled down, and when she saw him sitting on the box she said:

'Jacos Jack how short your shirt is! What are you at?'

He explained to her that the goose had gone off the eggs and that he was trying to keep the temperature up until she'd come back.

'Damn it, Moll' he said, 'I have *codladh grífín* in my two shins, and would you ever come up and put

72

down your hand and see is there anything happening!'

Moll came up, an innocent creature, and put her hand down.

'No Jack,' she said, 'there's no egg out yet. There's no shell broken. Oh wait!' she said all of a sudden. 'There's one out! And judging by the long neck on him I'd say he's a gander!'

At this moment the goose appeared at the door and when she saw who was sitting on her eggs, she bagan to flap her wings and with her neck stretched out in front of her and she came hissing at him. He was lucky to get through the room door without missing a piece out of his *sawtawn!*

Moll gathered herself out of the place, she didn't want to be there when the wife came in. He put on his clothes in the room and now he said he would have to attend to the next item which was to see to the bread. Blessed hour to night you could smell it. He took the cover off the oven and a *bocarum* of blue smoke came up. The cake was as black as the ace of spades inside. He was hammering the oven on the floor, no good, he had to go out in the yard and get the shovel to dig the cake out of the oven. That was another job gone wrong!

He said he'd get dinner for the working woman, when with that he heard the cow bellowing, he had forgotten to give her a drink. He took the reins off the churn, went out to the stall and put it on the cow's horns, she was a *bradaigh* cow, he couldn't let her loose. On his way to the stream, as he was passing the house, he looked up at the roof and there was a fine crop of grass corn growing on the thatch. It was on the thatch the likes of him would have it! He said to himself 'Waste not, want not!' And when he was coming back from the stream there was a *leaca* field at

73

the back of the house sloping up almost on one level with the roof. He walked the cow up the field and jumped her on to the thatch! Yerra, she didn't go down through it at all she was like a reindeer. The cow began to graze away delighted with herself. He was holding the rope and he said:

'I can't remain here all the time minding her, I have to get the dinner for the wife.'

He thought of another plan. He walked up the barge of the gable and let his end of the rope down the chimney; then he came inside, and took the rope, it was fine and long, and tied it around himself and put a knot on it. That was a great plan altogether, for he was minding the cow on the roof, and at the same time his hands were free to get the dinner for the working woman! Sometimes the cow, moving on the roof, would pull the rope up the chimney and draw him towards the fireplace. 'Yeoish!' he'd say to stop her. He put the spuds in the pan and he washed 'em, then he took the little skillet pot, the mouth of it no bigger than the mouth of my hat, and this was to be his cooking utensil. Things were going so well for him that he began to sing:

'When we got into London the police they were on the quay,

Bhí na barántaisí scríte san "Telegraph News" ó inné.[1]

With that the cow fell off the roof! The legs were taken from under him and he was swept feet first along the floor and up the chimney until he came to the narrow place, and he stuck there like a cork you'd try to pull with a cord out of a bottle. The cow was hanging down outside, and he was hanging down inside! And he had the pot in his hands all the time. If he let it fall it'd break — hadn't he enough damage

74

done!

There he remained till his wife was coming in from the field and when she saw the cow hanging down — her two hind legs in the yard and her two front legs up against the gable of the house, for all the world like the lads used be long 'go when the Black and Tans would be searching 'em — she ran up with the spade and cut the rope. The cow fell down and ran away and when there was nothing to balance him the man fell down the chimney for she heard him shouting. She ran into the kitchen and there he was standing on his head in the pot!

She helped her husband out of the fireplace and put him sitting on a chair. But if she lost Kate and the child she couldn't get his head out of the pot. It was down over his ears. Now, it is a simple enough operation to break a pot, but it is a horse of a different colour if there's a man's head in it. It was in the village of Cullen it happened and the poor woman had to take him by the hand three miles to the forge. As she was going along the road people were running out to the doors, and when they saw this man with the strange headgear they thought he was the advance guard of an invading army! They were following after her, the young blackguards laughing, and saying:

'How did he get his head into the pot?'

She was so vexed that she said: 'He was trying to see was there a hole in the bottom of it.'

When she got him to the forge the smith, and a very awkward man too, hit him a belt of a sledge hammer breaking the pot into flitters and turning his head sideways until his jaw rested on his left shoulder. Whatever damage was done to the vertibrae the poor man was landed with a permanent crick in his neck, and the woman was a bigger show coming home with

She helped her husband out of the fireplace...

him than she was going! And people wanted to know, what it was he was looking back at? She brought him to the City for nine mornings running and each morning after the round he drank at the holy well. There was a small rubbing stone there that time, no bigger than a pigeon's egg, and each morning when he had taken the sup at the well the woman used to rub the curing stone to the outside of his neck, and as far down as she could get it on the inside so that nothing'd be ovelooked. Blast me if the *amadán* didn't close his mouth on her on the ninth morning and swallowed the relic! With the effort he had to make to get it down past his Adam's apple he turned his neck and he was cured!

She took him by the hand then and brought him down Shrone, over Rathbeag, through Rathmore and into the village of Cullen. They went the lower road, I came the high road; they crossed by the stepping stones; I came over the bridge; they were drowned and I was saved, but all I ever got out of my storytelling was shoes of brown paper and stockings of thick milk; I only know what I heard; I only heard what was said and a lot of what was said was that Knock finished the holy well!

1. The warrants had been published in yesterday's 'Telegraph News'.

77

THE SEASON OF LIGHT

As well as pattern day there is one other religious observance of long ago worth recalling. I'm thinking of Christmas. No word of a lie but it was something to write home about when I was small. Oh! the way we looked forward to twilight on Christmas Eve, for when darkness fell it was Christmas Night, the greatest night of all the year. We youngsters would be up with the crack of dawn that morning to have the house ready for the night.

Berry holly would have to be cut and brought in to deck out the windows, the top of the dresser, the back of the settle and the clevvy. We'd bring in ivy too and put a sprig of laurel behind the pictures, above the lintel of the door and around the fireplace. But we wouldn't overdo it, or if we did my mother would make us cut it down a bit, reminding us that she'd like to feel that she was in her own house for Christmas, and not in the middle of a wood!

Well, the transformation we could bring about in the kitchen with all that greenery! But we weren't finished yet. The Christmas candles had to be prepared; these were of white tallow as thick as the handle of a spade and nearly as tall. In some houses they'd scoop out a hole in a turnip and put the candle sitting into it. A big crock we'd use. We'd put the candle standing into that and pack it around with sand. If you hadn't sand, bran or pollard would do.

When the candle was firm in position we'd spike sprigs of holly or laurel into the sand about the candle, and we had coloured paper too to put around the outside of the crock to take the bare look off it. With that same coloured paper, the girls in the family, if they were anyway handy, could make paper flowers to decorate the holly. Then what would cap it all, was a length of young ivy and spiral it up around the candle — it looked lovely! That done, we would go through the same manoeuvre until there was a candle in a crock for every window in the house.

Then we'd be praying for night to fall, for you couldn't see the right effect until the candles were lit. That honour would fall to the youngest in the house. My father would lift him up saying: 'In the name of the Father and of the Son . . .' and when the child had blessed himself, he would put the lighting spill to the candle, and from that candle the other candles would be lit, and we'd be half daft with excitement, enjoying the great blaze of light, and running from the rooms to the kitchen and out into the yard to see what the effect was like from the outside. When we'd get tired of looking at the candles in our own windows, we'd turn and try to name the neighbours' houses as the bunches of lights came on, two windows here and three windows there, across the dark countryside and away up to the foot of the hills. And as sure as anything someone'd be late and we'd rush into my mother saying:

'Faith, then there's no light on yet in Rosacrew!'

'Go on ye're knees!' my mother would say. The time she'd pick for the Rosary, just as the salt ling was ready and the white onion sauce and the potatoes steaming over the fire. But I suppose there'd be no religion in the world only for the women. The Rosary in our house didn't end at five decades. Not at all.

After the Hail Holy Queen my mother would branch into the Trimmings:

'Come Holy Ghost send down those beams,
Which sweetly flow in silent streams'.

She'd pray for everyone in sickness and in need: the poor souls and the sinful soul that was at that very moment trembling before the Judgement seat above. She'd pray for the sailor on the seas: 'Protect him from the tempest, Oh Lord, and bring him safely home'. And the lone traveller on the highway and of course our emigrants and, last of all, the members of her own family:

> 'God bless and save us all.
> St Patrick, Bridget and Colmcille
> Guard each wall.
> May the Queen of heaven
> And the angels bright
> Keep us and our house
> From all harm this night!'

Our knees'd be aching as we got up off the floor, and it would take my father a while to get the prayer arch out of his back. Well, we wouldn't be sitting down to the supper when my mother'd bless herself again, a preliminary to grace before meals, and you could hardly blame my father for losing his patience.

'Is it in a monastery we are?' he'd say. 'Haven't we done enough praying for one night?'

After the supper there was Christmas cake for anyone with a sweet tooth. My father'd never look at that. His eye'd be on the big earthenware jar below the dresser, and it would be a great relief to him when my mother'd say to us:

'Go out there, one of ye, and tell the neighbouring

men to come in for a while.'

It was the custom that night, Nollaig Mhór, big Christmas, for the men to visit each other's houses. The women were too busy to be bothered. They had their own night, 'Nollaig na mBan,' small Christmas, for making tapes. In a while's time the men'd come, and at the first lag in the conversation my father'd take the cork off the jar and fill out a few cups of porter. The men, by the way, not noticing what was going on, and then when they'd get the cups, all surprise they'd say:

'What's this? What's this for?'

'Go on take it,' my father'd say. 'It is Christmas night, neighbours, and more luck to us!'

Then the men's faces'd light up and lifting their cups they'd say:

'Happy Christmas, Ned. Happy Christmas, Hannie. Happy Christmas, everyone!'

'And the same to ye men,' my father would answer. 'May we all be alive again this time twelve months.'

And my mother, who was never very happy in the presence of strong drink, would direct her gaze in the direction of the Christmas candle and say:

'The grace of God to us all!'

After sampling the beverage one of the men putting out his lower lip to suck in any stray particles of froth that had lodged in his moustache would inquire:

'Where did you get this, Ned?'

'Carthy Dannehy's,' my father'd say.

'He always keeps a good drop, I'll say that for him.'

'Sláinte, Ned,' from all the men.

'Sláinte chugat is cabhair
Dealbh go deo ná rabhair,
Is go bhfásfaidh gach ribín
Ar do cheann chomh fada le meigeal ghabhair.'

81

(Health to you and support. May you never be destitute. And may every rib (of hair) on your head grow to be as long as a goat's beard).

That was the poet's toast only, of course, it wasn't as mild as that. I wouldn't expose ye to the full blast of it!

Eoghan Rua Ó Súilleabháin was the poet best remembered in our district, and no Christmas night would pass that he wouldn't be drawn down. Eoghan Rua it seems was out walking one day and he called into a farmer's house. An only daughter is all the farmer had and he was on the look-out for a *cliamhain isteach* for her. But the farmer would not be satisfied with any son-in-law, only a young man that could talk English.

That was a stiff enough proposition at the time, two hundred years ago, for Irish was the common language of the country. So the farmer, in dread of his life that he'd be left with the daughter idle on his hands, told his story to Eoghan Rua, and he told it to the right man when he told it to Eoghan!

'I know the very man,' Eoghan said, 'that'd suit you down to the ground. A fine, strapping, honest boy, but I don't think he have any fortune.'

'Don't mind that,' the farmer said. 'I'll ask no money with him if he can talk the English.'

'Well now,' says Eoghan, 'the way it is the English isn't good by him and on the other hand the English isn't bad by him.'

'Bring him here to the house until I see him,' the farmer said.

Eoghan went off and he didn't stop until he found a fine, deserving, young lad working alone in a field. Eoghan took him home, put him into a good suit and gave a few days teaching him just enough English to be able to answer a question in that language, for Irish was all the boy had. When the young man had mastered the piece of English, Eoghan and himself set

82

out for the farmer's house. There was a big crowd there, all talking away in Irish. The young lad made off the farmer's daughter, a nice little mallet of a one, and in no time the two were canoodling in the corner. Out in the night Eoghan told the young man to go out in the yard and see what the weather was doing, and when he was gone Eoghan said to the farmer:

'I suppose you'd like to hear this fellow talking English?

'Isn't that what he's here for,' says the farmer.

'He's gone outside,' says Eoghan, 'to see what the night is doing, so I'll test him for you when he comes in.'

When the gorsoon had done whatever he had to do outside he straightened back into the house.

'Well, friend,' says Eoghan, 'and what are the climatic conditions abroad?'

The young lad halted. Then he threw back his shoulders and with one eye on the farmer's daughter, he said:

'From my astronomical observations, my reckoning and my calculations, from the constant rolling of the firmament, the dismal aspect of the stars and the widespread fermentation of the atmosphere, I prognosticate a heavy discharge from the clouds!' Well, the farmer was there and his mouth opened so wide you could put a turnip into it.

'Oh,' says he, 'what a sweet sound English makes. I'd stay listening to it till the crack of doom!' My clown! He thought he had a professor of Trinity Hall standing there on the floor. There was no trouble about making the match, but they weren't too long married when the farmer found out that that was all the English the young man had. He was mad, fit to be tied. The daughter made no complaint. She was happy out with him as he was.

Came the big fair in Castleisland and the farmer was there standing to a few *budógs*, when who should he see passing but Eoghan Rua singing one of his new compositions. The farmer ran after him and caught him by the two lapels of his coat saying:

'You worthless blackguard! The way you fooled me.'

'Cool down, boy,' says Eoghan to him. 'Don't be running away with yourself! What did I do to you?'

'Didn't you tell me,' says the farmer, 'that the son-in-law you landed me with knew English?'

'I said no such thing,' says Eoghan. 'Toughen now, control yourself. Didn't I say to you that the English wasn't good by him?'

'You did,' says the farmer.

'And didn't I say to you the English wasn't bad by him?'

'You did,' says the farmer.

'And didn't I say to you so,' says Eoghan, 'that he had no English *good* nor *bad!*'

'A bit of a boyo,' was how my mother used to describe Eoghan, and reflecting on the story as the men laughed, she'd say half to herself half to the fire: 'Or was he ever there?'

In every house on Christmas night there'd be a big log of elm or ash stretched behind the fire. It'd reach from the leg of the crane to the opposite pier with wet moss and strands of ivy still clinging to it. When the fire got going good, little jets of steam'd come hissing out of the log, and there'd be an occasional minor explosion which'd make the cat jump. He would eye the spot where the sound came from for a while, and then decide it might be safer back a piece. As time went on such would be the heat from the burning log that we'd all take a leaf out of the cat's book and move back.

The shuffling of the chairs'd bring about a pause in the conversation during which the men would remark on the quality of the Christmas log, some of them might remember the growing tree of which it formed

84

part. The men would admire the decorations and compliment us young lads on our ingenuity. Then looking at the holly they'd say it was a sign of a mild winter when the blackbirds hadn't all the berries gone.

The men wouldn't stay all night in the one place. A neighbour getting to his feet'd say:

'Come on away down to our house until we sample what my woman brought from town. It'll have to be good to be up to this drop!'

Later on we'd have to go and collect my father so that he'd be in some shape for the chapel in the morning. We youngsters loved going to Mass in the dark and hearing the sound of the horses' hooves and the crack of the car axles if the morning was frosty, the loud greetings outside the chapel gate, people bumping into one another in the darkness.

'That you Mary? Happy Christmas to you!'

'Same to you!' Mary'd say. And then she'd add under her breath: 'The devil turn you. Will you watch where you are going, or do you want to floor me!'

When we were bigger we were let go to midnight Mass in the Friary. Two Third Order men at the door. Very officious, sniffing in case anyone got in with a sign of drink on him. Christmas Day'd be quiet. There'd be a goose for the dinner, or a cock. There was post that time on Christmas Day and every house the postman'd go into, especially if he had a letter from America, he'd have to take a nip. At the end of his round the poor man'd be stocious. What harm was that. He'd be sober and correct for the rest of the year!

Once you got into long trousers and had a few bob in your pocket, what you looked forward to was Stephen's Night. All'd hit for the village. A big night of dancing. Even before the returned Yanks built the dance halls there'd be dancing in the kitchen of the public house. 'Twas Ned Connor that'd be on the concertina and he was a gifted player, but like many musicians he liked the drop. Ned was noted. The wife warned him one Christmas Eve to be sure and go to confession. Ned forgot all about it until he was passing the Friary on the way home good and full, and seeing the goldy cross on the gate out of the corner of his eye, he was reminded of it and he went in.

Sliding along the seat as those before him moved towards the confessional, he finally got to the box and went in. It can be stuffy enough inside there when old people are in and out, and whoever was at the other side had a long story to tell, so that the fumes of the drink rising in Ned's head made him drowsy and he nodded off. When the shutter came across with a bang, he woke up, and said:

'The same again and turn on the light in the snug!'

That Christmas night the wife's aunt, Auntie Pegg, was visiting 'em, a fierce druidess of a one, and she wasn't long in pointing out to Ned the error of his ways. She made him go down on his knees and promise he'd give up the drink, the ruination of body and soul! So he went into the Mercy Convent and took the pledge from Sister Benedict. And to everyone's surprise kept it — well, until one day he met some old comrades in town. He didn't want to go into the public house but they said it would only be the *one*. He came out of the place legless, he was so bad when he got into his own house he had to hold on to the back of the chair to maintain any relationship with the perpendicular.

His wife's aunt came down the stairs in her night attire, and standing on the bottom step, her hand on the newel post, she read him a lesson:

'A nice state to be in after the promise he gave to his wife and to his children and to myself and to the Man above! And look at the *geatch* of him now,' she said. 'Look at him now, his face puffed and bloated! His soul as black as porter! And what would you do,' she said to him, 'if the Lord called on you this minute?'

'To tell you the truth, auntie,' he said, 'I couldn't stir a leg!'

THE BAREFOOTED GANDER

There were more people around the place at Christmas time. Boys and girls home from service strolling up and down the road at night or talking in bunches under the light spilling out from the windows.

The rambling house would be fuller too with maybe a visitor or two back from New York. Well I remember the year John Murphy came home. He handed out American cigarettes to everyone, which were accepted, as the man said, with avidity. I partly guessed from the way he was smiling that there was some trick in it. We all lit up and the next minute the fags began to explode! The men pulled them out of their mouths, but they exploded again in their hands, so they threw them on the floor filling the kitchen with fireworks. The older men were palming their moustaches fearing they had been blown off! We laughed enough that night and as the smoke cleared the talk turned to America and the boat trip which put our storyteller in mind of an attempt to fly the Atlantic long before the Wright brothers were born.

There was a man living one time not a hundred miles from where I'm sitting and his name was Timmie Warren. He was working for his day's hire drawing goods from the Railway Station for a big shopkeeper. He had good wages for the time it was, a house of his own, a nice wife and enough to ate, and wouldn't you think he'd be satisfied. He was not! For whatever little deficiency was in the top storey he never dreamt in his

...and the next minute the fags began to explode!

life. Whether he slept on his left side or on his right side, on his back or on his bread basket — 'twas all the one, he got up in the morning the same as he went to bed the night before, with no story to tell.

Now, this mightn't bother you or it mightn't bother me, but it did bother Timmie Warren, for in the place he was working, after the dinner every day the other workmen would be telling him about the grand dreams they had the night before. Places they visited, things they saw, the tall buildings and the different coloured people walking on painted flag-stones. The banquets they were at, the wine, the food and the company ... until they had Timmie Warren driven demented and he was losing the colour. So he went along and he spoke to 'Discount'. That was the shopkeeper's nickname, for his motto was, 'Take a pound's worth and I'll throw off a bob.' And as prime a boyo he was as you'd meet from here to the town of Tallow. So when he heard Timmie Warren's tale of woe about not being able to dream, he smiled and said:

'If every riddle was as easy unravelled as that life'd be heaven. All you have to do when you go home this evening is to put out the fire, bring the bed down out of the room and set it up inside in the fireplace. Retire there for the night, and if you aren't dreaming before morning, my name is not 'Discount!' When Timmie Warren heard that, 'twas like as if he was left a legacy, he went home delighted, but it took him from then until ten o'clock that night to convince his wife to fall in with his plan — *ní nach ionadh!*

'And,' says she, 'if the soot falls down on the bedclothes, is it you'll be dancing on 'em below in the *glaise?* And isn't soft the wool grows on you, if you expect your wife to fall in with every daft notion that comes into your head.'

But if I didn't say it before, I'll say it now, there's great credit due to the wives of Ireland and the pains they'll go to to humour a cranky husband. Finally, she fell in with his wishes. The fire was put out, the bed was brought down out of the room and set up inside in the fireplace, and the two retired for the night.

Timmie Warren was not too long asleep when he thought he heard a knock at the door and a voice saying:

'Get up, Timmie Warren and take this letter to America.'

'Hah,' says Timmie, 'what's that?'

'Get up,' says the voice, 'and take this letter to America.'

'Who's there?' says Timmie.

''Tis me, "Discount". Get up and take this letter to America.'

Timmie got into his Sunday clothes and his velour hat, stuck his legs into his shoes, took the letter and ran off in the direction of America. He kept going, the tips on his heels knocking fire out of the road until he came to the broad Atlantic ocean. And there he saw this big white gander with his shoes off paddling.

'Hello, Timmie Warren', says the gander. Ganders could talk then. 'Where are you off to?'

'I'm going to America,' says Timmie, 'with this letter for "Discount", but the trouble is how am I going to get over?'

'Well,' says the gander, 'if every riddle was as easy unravelled as that life'd be heaven, hop up on my back and I'll fly you over.'

'I'm not too heavy for you,' says Timmie when he had himself settled.

'You're heavy enough, then,' says the gander. 'But we'll chance it now.'

And he flapped his wings and craned his neck, made one bounce and up he soared and away he flew. No more bother! And the lovely soft seat Timmie Warren had, and the view! He was in his element looking down on the world, and 'twasn't long until he was singing:

When I was young and in my bloom,
My mind was ill at ease;
I was dreaming of Amerikay
And gold beyond the seas.

Everything went smack smooth 'till they were half way across the Atlantic, when the gander said:

'Hop down off my back, Timmie Warren.'

'Hah,' says Timmie, 'what's that your saying to me?'

'Hop down off my back. I'm winded!'

'Hop down where?' says Timmie. 'Have you any *splink?* Where can I hop down to?'

'Hop down off my back,' says the gander, 'I can't fly another peg.'

'I will not,' says Timmie.

And a fierce argument cropped up between them, and the result of it was that the gander flew out from under Timmie Warren and left him falling down through the air. He was in a nice pucker now, the poor man!

Well, as luck should have it, it so happened that the Clare team were flying out to America to play New York, at a lower level of course! And where did Timmie Warren fall but down into the middle of 'em, and grabbed on to the goalie's hurley.

'Take go now,' says the goalie, 'or I'll give you a tap.' And he would in a minute!

'Ah, let me hold on for a small piece till the gander gets his second wind,' says Timmie.

He was in a nice pucker now, the poor man!

'Take go,' says the goalie, 'you're only holding us up and we'll be late for the line-out. Do you want us to lose the match?'

'I do not,' says Timmie.

And he looked down to see how far he'd have to fall and wasn't there a ship nearly under him in the ocean.

'Throw yourself down,' says the captain of the ship, 'and we'll catch you.'

'How do I know,' says Timmie, 'but 'tis into the waves I'll fall and be drowned.'

'Can't you throw down one of your shoes,' says the captain, 'and we'll see where it will land.'

Timmie kicked off one of his shoes and with that there was an unmerciful yell from his wife.

'Is that you, Sile,' says Timmie.

'What's left of me,' says she. 'Where are you?'

'Wherever I am,' says Timmie, 'I can't lead or drive. Strike a light!'

She lit a candle, and where was Timmie? Half way up the chimney, with one shoe off and one shoe on! She knew then what hit her.

'Come down,' says she, 'you cracked *criceálaí*. What a dreamer I have in you.'

He came down, and by the time he had the soot out of himself, out of the suit, and out of the bedclothes he didn't care if he never dreamt again and he to live to be as old as Methuselah!

Small Christmas Eve the women'd get together for a party. They might come into our place for a bit and then my mother'd go off with 'em to another house. One night it was awful late when my mother came in, and my father said to her:

'Where were you?'

'Out there,' she said. She didn't say anymore.

The decorations weren't taken down until the

morning after small Christmas Day. Any small lads who hadn't yet seen the crib, the mothers would take 'em in to the Friars' chapel that day. There was a brother from Belgium in the Friary then, and he was a pure dinger when it came to setting up a crib. The stable was very well brought out by him, with the Infant there and His mother and Saint Joseph of course. He had it nice and bright so that you could see half the town of Bethlehem sloping away from you. And all the animals that were there wherever he got 'em! Cows, very nearly as big as you'd see in the field, and sheep and the ass. You'd see angels flying overhead, shepherds below and the wise kings making their way in at the side. After saying a prayer the people'd pitch money into the stable as near as they could get it to the cradle. And by the time the crib was taken down the Infant'd be lying on a copper bed speckled with silver. That was how highly the people thought of the brother's work. You'd see nothing like it now anywhere.

GLOSSARY

a bhuachaill — boy
ábhar — amount
amadán — fool

badaoi, badaoi, badaoi — idiom used to call geese
bád sí — fairy boat
balbhán — dummy
bean Chonnachtach —Connacht woman
bean sí — fairy-woman
beart — bundle
bocarum — puff
braddy (bradaigh) — a thieving cow
budógs (bodóga) — heifers

ceol sí — fairy music
ciotóg — a left-handed person
cliabh — basket
cliamhain isteach — son in law
codladh grífín — pins and needles
collops (colpaí) — calves *(of legs)*
corp 'on diabhal — the corpse to the devil *(a curse)*
cúllochta — a side- or back- loft
cúlóg — one who rides behind another on horseback

dorns — fistfuls
drúcteens (drúchtíní) — beads *(of perspiration)*

éirí in airde gan cur leis — unmitigated vanity

fol-a-me-ding — something that defies description

gansey — jersey
geatch (geaits) — caper
gimp — urge
giobals (giobail) —rags
gíocs — a sound
glaise — stream
grá — love

kippens (cipíní) — sticks

lasaid — wooden baking board
leaca — sloping

méagram — headache
meigeall — a goat's beard
mo léir! — alas!
mo léir cráite! — woeful sorrow!
mothal — a mop of hair

ní nach ionadh! — and no wonder!

piseog(a) — superstition(s)
púcaí — bogey-men

sawtawn — bottom
scrat — stitch
skillawn (sciollán) — the portion of potato containing 'eye' or seed
   for planting
splink (I. splanc) — spark (of sense)
sugawn (súgán) — a hay or straw rope

teip — mark

whist (éist) — listen

yeoish! — steady!